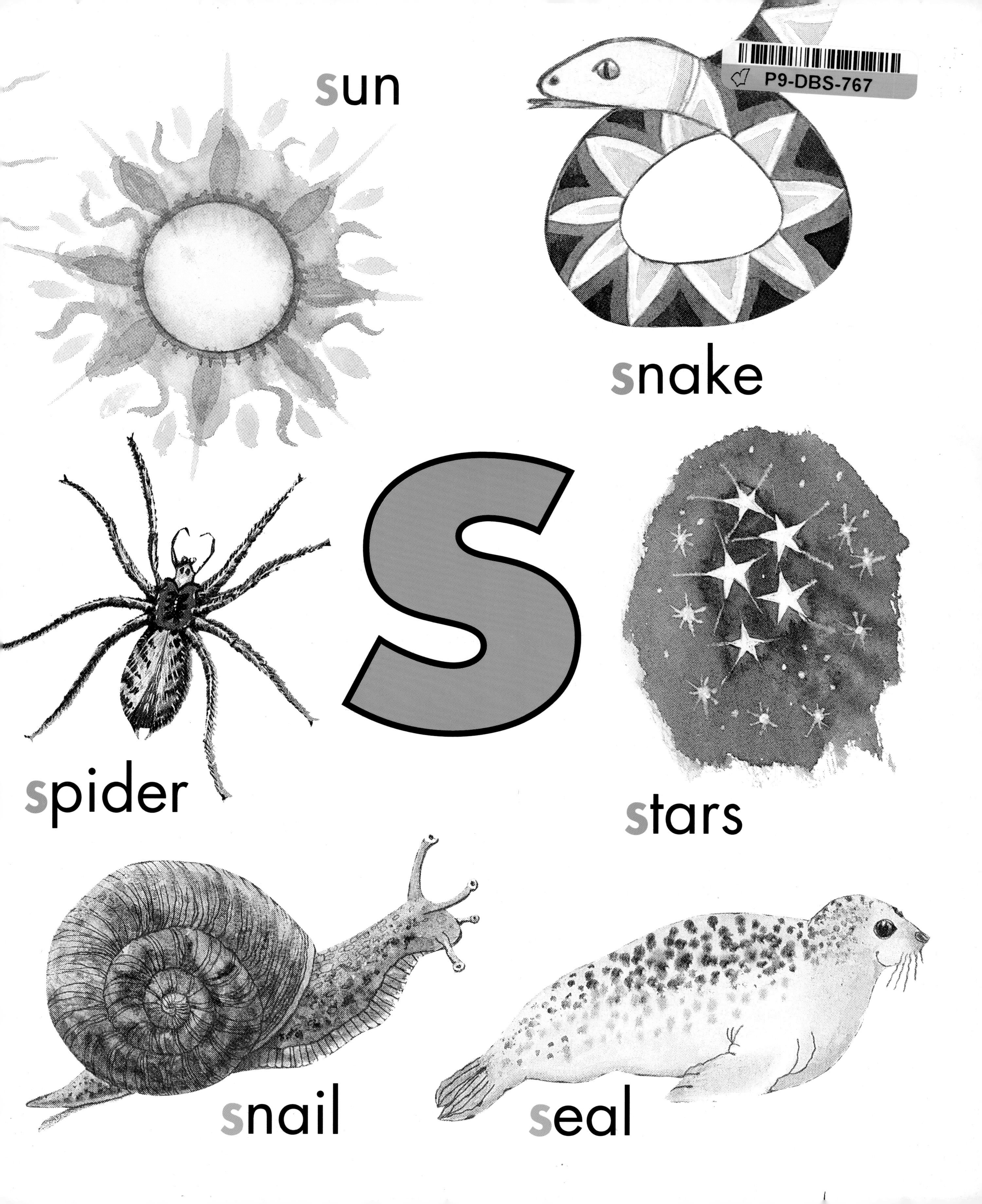
sun
snake
S
spider
stars
snail
seal

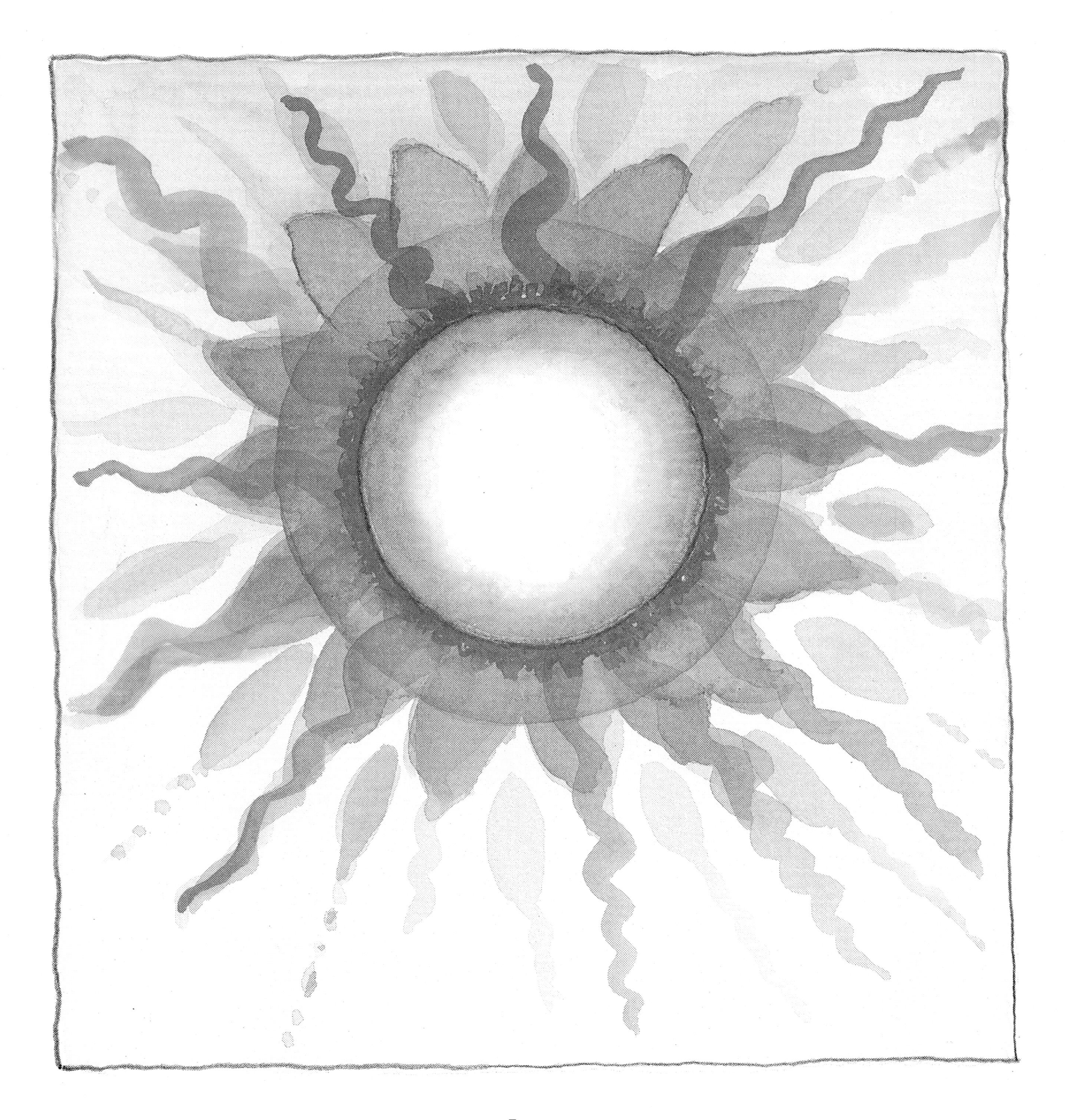

See the sun.

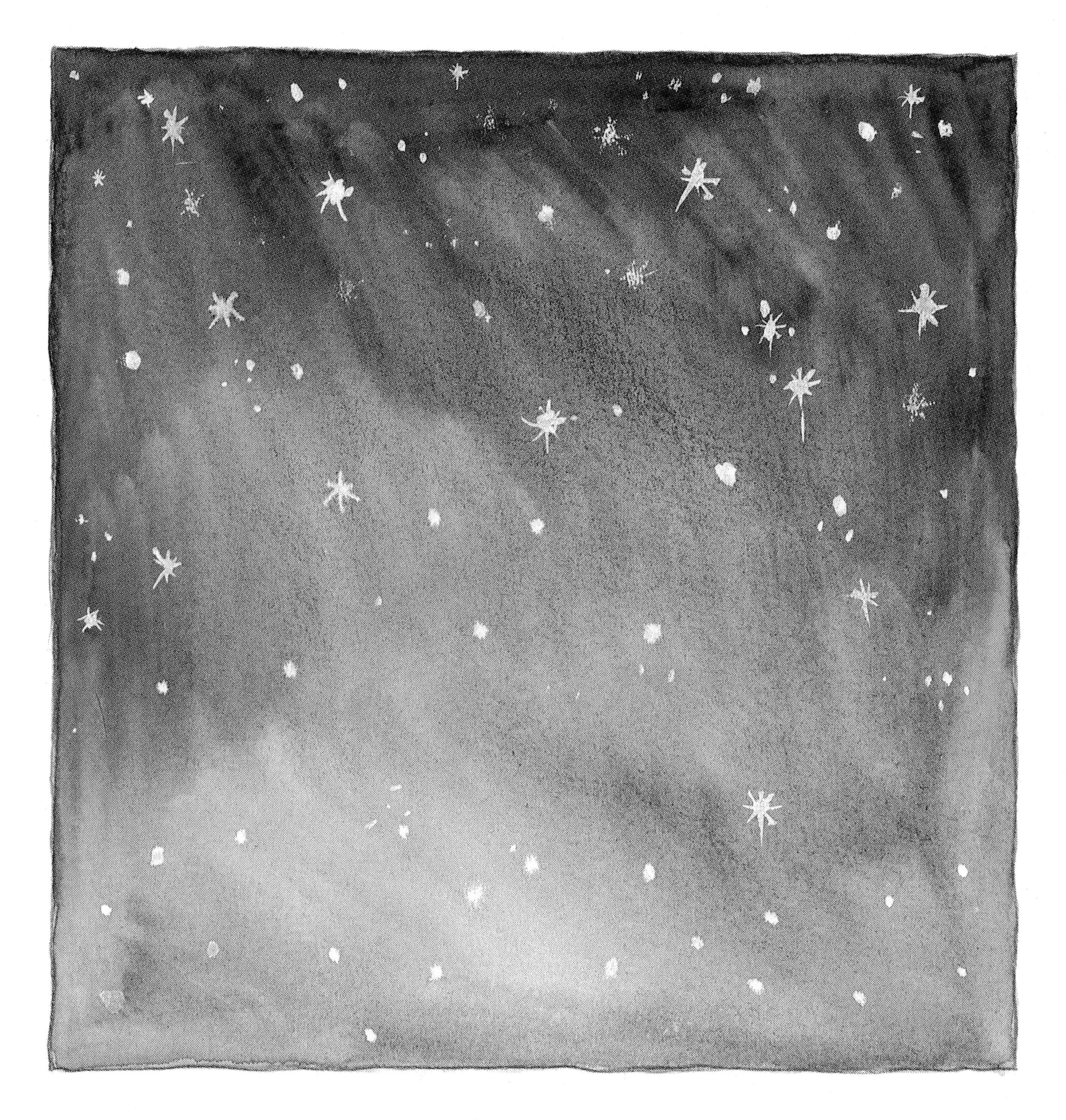

See the stars.

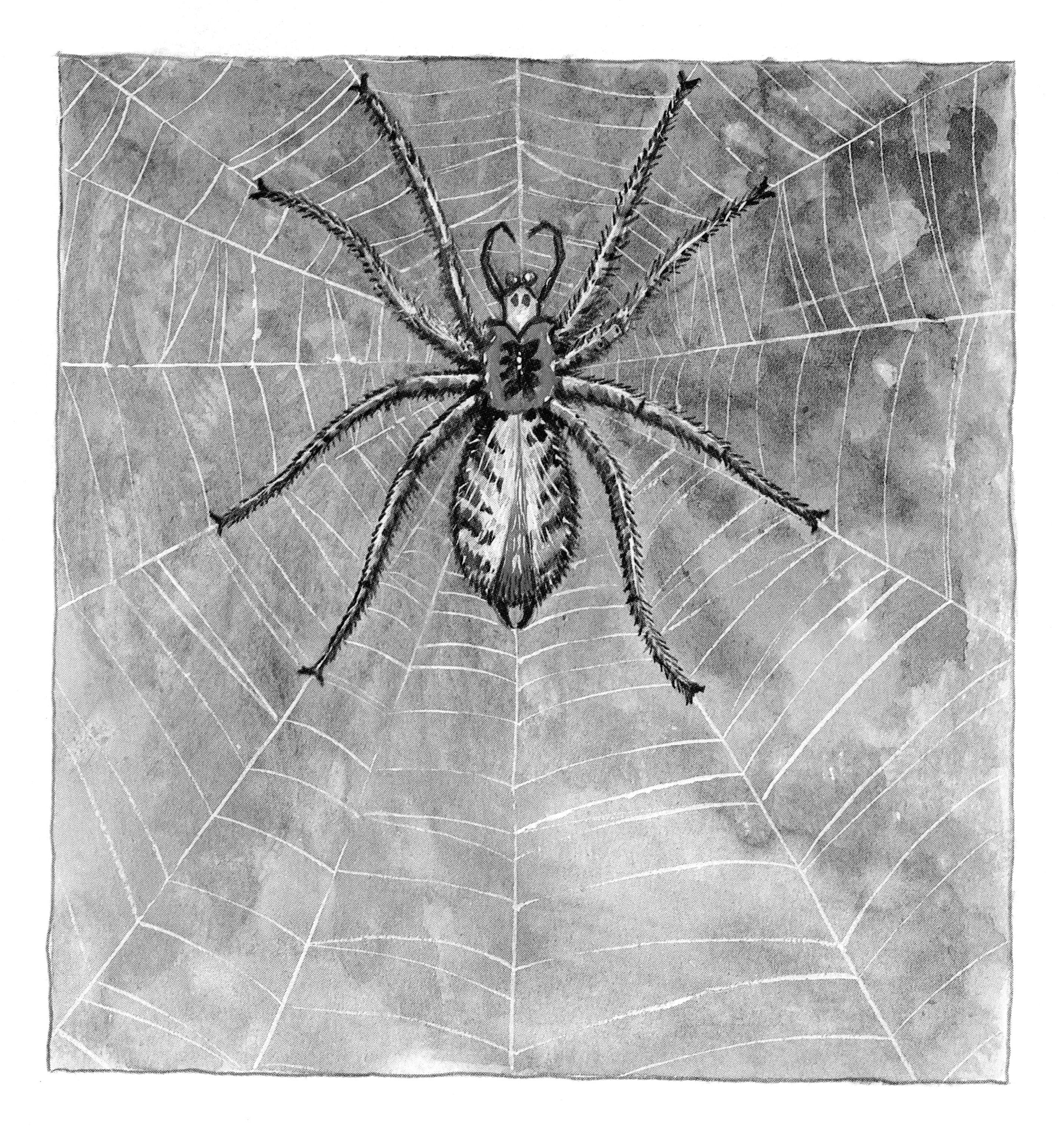

See the spider.

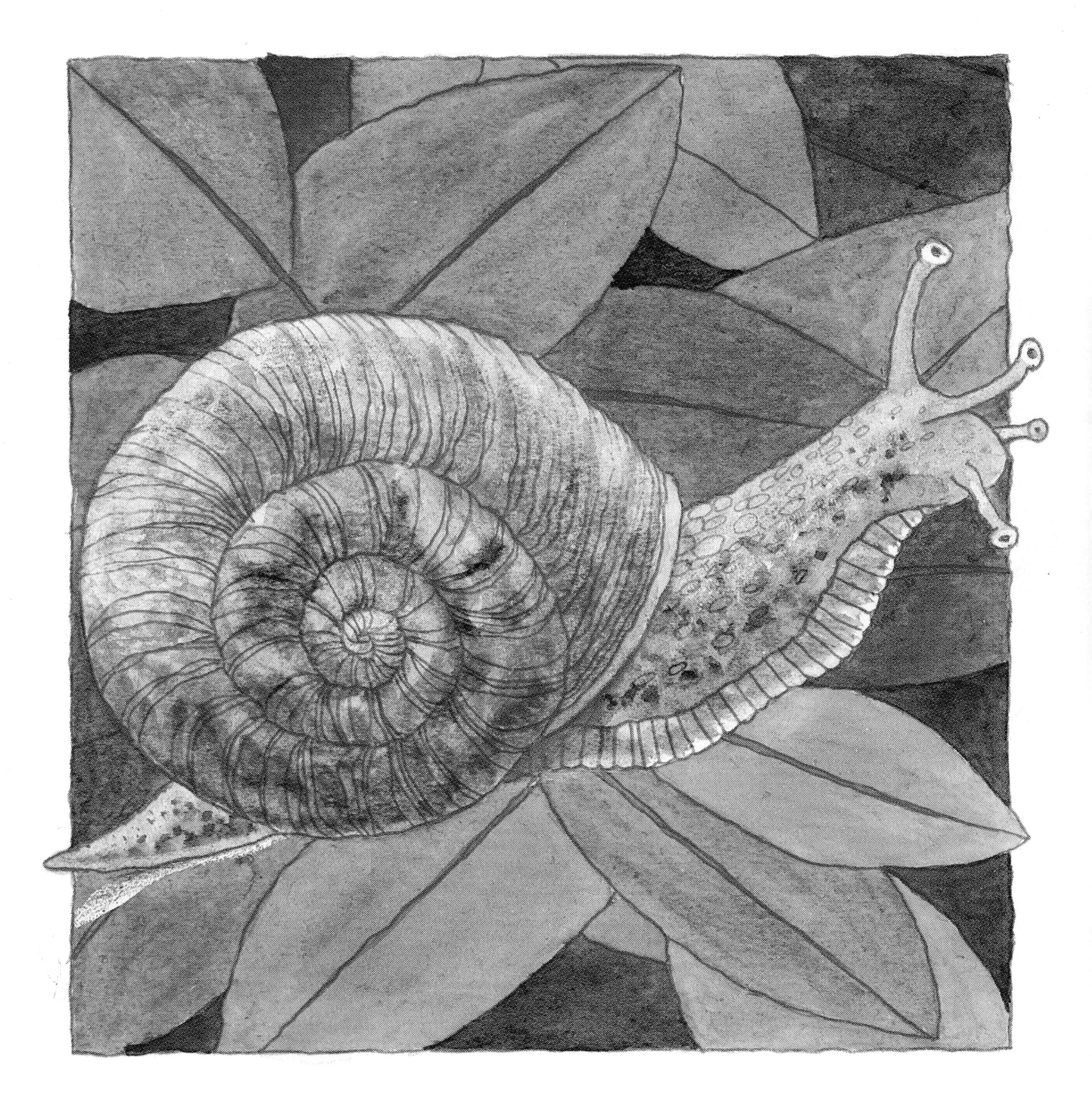

See the snail.

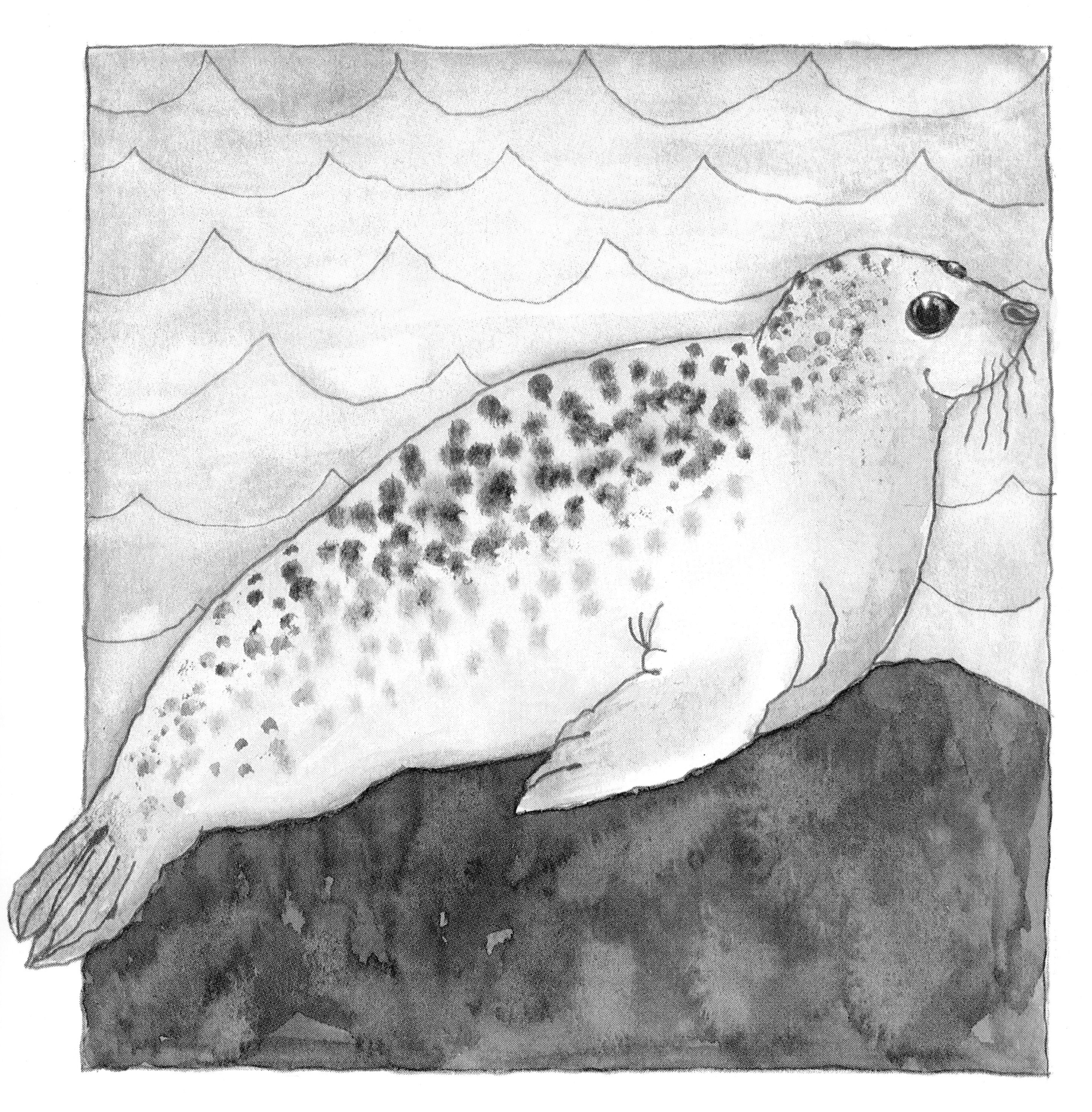

See the seal.

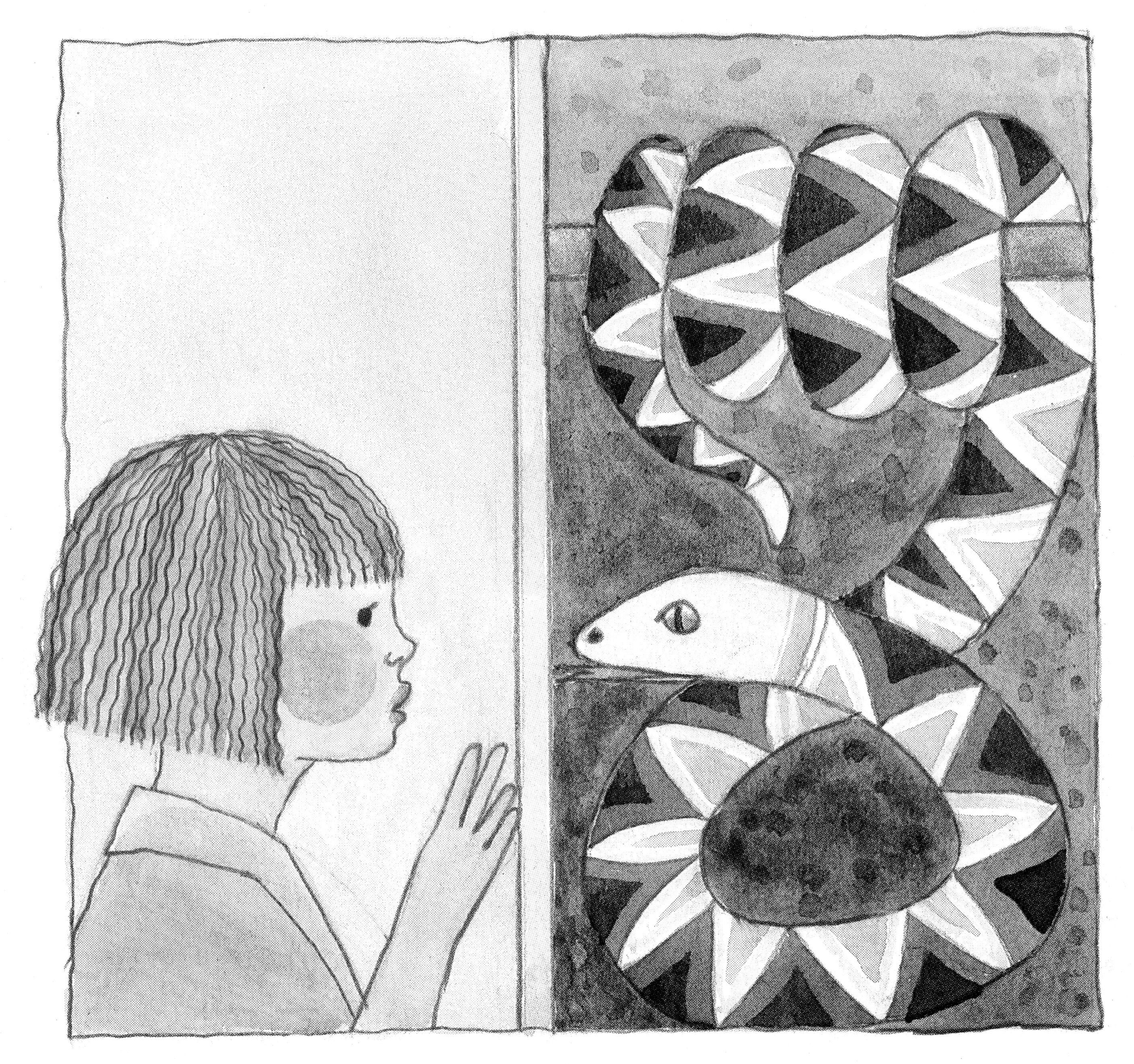

See the snake . . .
Sssssss!

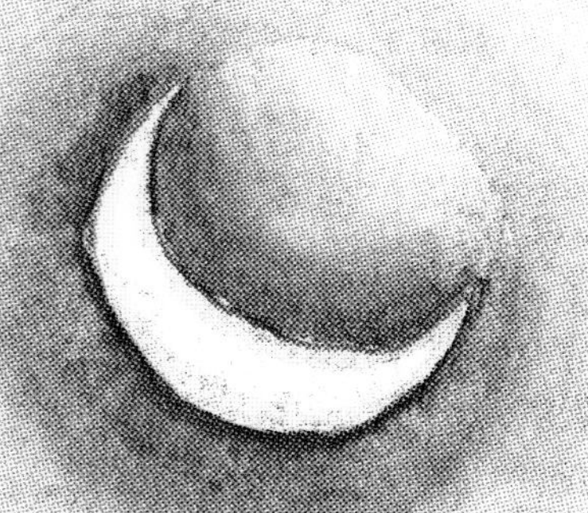

Sally go round
the sun.
Sally go round
the moon.
Sally go round
the chimney pots
on a Sunday afternoon.

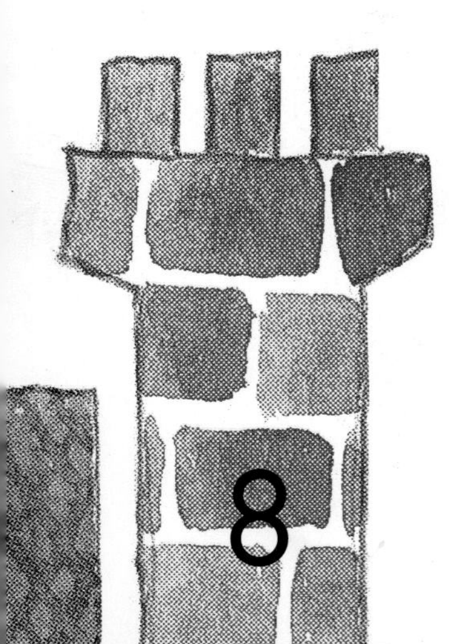